Usborne

Little Coloring
Christmas

Illustrated by Jenny Brown

Words by Kirsteen Robson

A Christmas
tree with
decorations

Christmas
presents
with ribbons
and bows

An angel
decoration

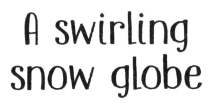

A swirling snow globe

A Santa hat

A shining
star

A toy
soldier

A stocking
full of
presents

A pair of new
ice skates

A house
in the snow

A painted
toy engine

A noisy
drum

A bear in
a hat

A happy
penguin

Sweet
candy canes

Spicy gingerbread

A squirrel
scampering
up a tree

Holly has
prickly leaves.

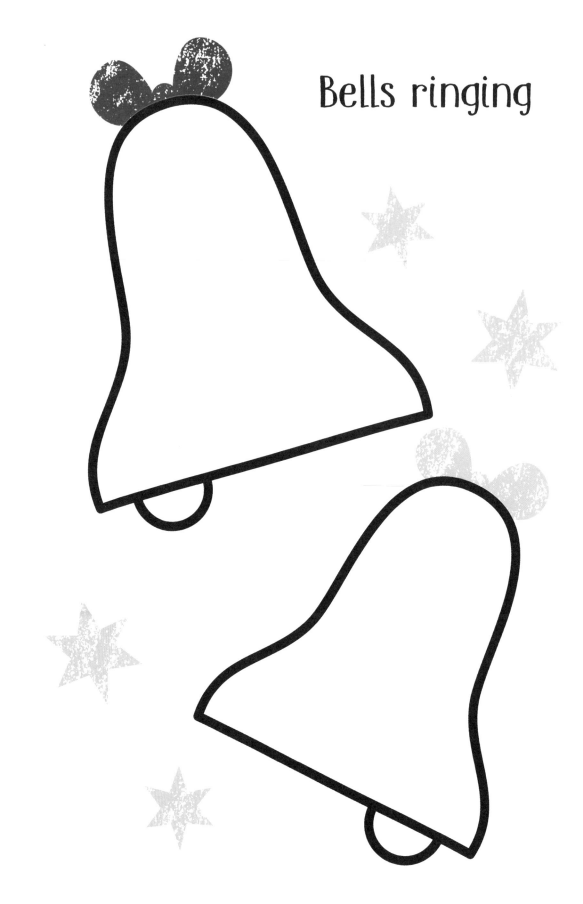

Bells ringing

A bird singing

Santa
wears red.

Rudolph the reindeer

A cupcake
with frosting

Hot chocolate with marshmallows and sprinkles

A sleeping fox

A merry elf

An owl on
a branch

Dangling
decorations

A seal sitting on the ice

A smiling
snowman

A gingerbread house